Yo veo 1 perro.

Yo veo 2 pájaros.

Yo veo 3 conejos.

Yo veo 4 ranas.

Yo veo 5 ratones.

¡Yo veo mucha diversión!

Versión en español por Queta Fernandez

Text copyright © 2004 by Scholastic Inc.
Illustrations copyright © 2004 by John Ueland.
Spanish translation copyright © 2004 by Scholastic Inc.
All rights reserved. Published by Scholastic Inc.
Printed in the U.S.A.

ISBN 0-439-68465-X

SCHOLASTIC and associated logos and designs are trademarks and/or registered trademarks of Scholastic Inc.

11 12 13 14 15 16 17 18   08   19 18 17 16 15 14

SCHOLASTIC INC.
New York   Toronto   London   Auckland   Sydney
Mexico City   New Delhi   Hong Kong   Buenos Aires